Rabbit

Jakki Wood

W
FRANKLIN WATTS
NEW YORK • LONDON • SYDNEY

If you choose me to be your rabbit –

I'm sure we'll soon be friends.

I will need my own special home called a hutch. Hutches have two rooms — one room for playing and eating,

and one room for sleeping. Fill it with clean straw so I can make a cosy nest.

I hate getting too cold or hot.
My hutch should be away from hot sun
and icy winds.

Remember to check my hutch every day and throw out any leftover food.
Please wash it out at least once a week.

As well as my hutch I will need...

carrying box

brush and comb

hay and sawdust to go
inside my hutch

heavy food bowl

mineral lick

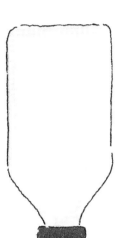

water bottle

hay in a hay rack. Hay is an important part of a rabbit's food. I need to eat it every day.

log to gnaw on. This keeps my teeth healthy and strong.

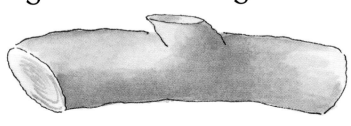

I need two meals a day. One should be special rabbit pellets. For my other meal I like fresh vegetables like cabbage, lettuce or carrots.

I love munching apples!

I also like to eat some weeds that grow outside. Don't forget I need fresh water every day.

dandelion   clover   plantain   chickweed

I love digging, but make sure I don't escape and get lost.

We can play together. My back legs are very strong, so I'm good at running,

hopping and jumping.

When you're not around I would still like to play outside. I need lots of exercise so I don't get fat. If I have a special run I can safely play out on my own.

Remember to use both hands when you pick me up. One hand to hold me around the back of my neck and the other to support me underneath.

Now scoop me up into your arms.

If I lick you it means I really like you.
I'm glad you chose me to be your friend.